Reading
Practice

PaRragon

Bath · New York · Cologne · Melbourne · Delhi
Hong Kong · Shenzhen · Singapore

Helping your child

⭐ The activities in this book will help your child to develop their reading skills.

⭐ Your child will gain confidence in decoding individual words independently and reading a wide range of poems, stories and non-fiction texts.

⭐ Your child will learn about trigraphs (three letters that make one sound), contractions (two words shortened into one word), homophones (words that sound the same, but have different meanings), and words ending with different suffixes. They will also learn about sequencing events of stories and non-fiction texts and will answer comprehension questions.

⭐ Set aside time to do the activities together. Do a little at a time so that your child enjoys learning.

⭐ Give lots of encouragement and praise. Use the gold stars as rewards and incentives.

⭐ The answers are on page 32.

This edition published by Parragon Books Ltd in 2016

Parragon Books Ltd
Chartist House
15-17 Trim Street
Bath BA1 1HA, UK
www.parragon.com

Written by Nina Filipek and Catherine Casey
Illustrated by Simon Abbot and Adam Linley
Educational Consultant: Geraldine Taylor

ISBN 978-1-4748-4740-7

Printed in China

Contents

Match the words 4

Match the trigraphs 5

Words ending in **ly** 6

Words ending in **ful** 7

Words ending in **ed** 8

Words to remember 9

Words that sound
the same 10

Silent letters 12

Adding **el**, **al** or **le** 13

Making sense 14

Ordering sentences 15

Missing letters 16

Ordering instructions 17

What am I? 18

Who is who? 19

Reading a poem 20

Reading a story 22

Understanding a story 24

Reading information 26

Making predictions 28

Solve the mystery 30

Answers 32

Match the words

Read the descriptions in the boxes below. Draw a ring around the description that matches each picture.

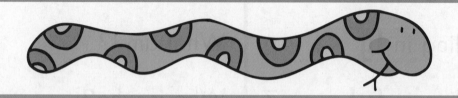

a stripy snake   **a spotty snake**

a blue shoe

a brown shoe

a clean piglet

a muddy piglet

Note for parent: This activity allows your child to blend phonemes (sounds) to decode words.

Match the trigraphs

Draw a line to match each word to the sound that is found in it.

scare

night

right

dare

chair

hear

are

igh

air

pair

ear

near

before

ore

more

hair

Note for parent: A trigraph is three letters that make one sound. For trexample: ore, ear, are.

5

Words ending in **ly**

Read the sentences below. Look at the picture and choose the correct word to complete each sentence. Write the words on the lines.

The dog barked _____.

neatly / loudly

The snow fell _____.

clearly / heavily

He did his homework _____.

carefully / cuddly

The queen was _____.

friendly / likely

Note for parent: In this activity your child is reading words with the common suffix 'ly'. A suffix is a group of letters used at the end of a word to turn it into another word.

Words ending in **ful**

Read the words below each box. Draw a picture in each box to match the word.

powerful

tearful

cheerful

beautiful

Note for parent: In this activity your child is reading words with the common suffix 'ful'.

7

Words ending in **ed**

Read the words in the box. Act out each word and ask a grown-up to guess what it is.

> **buzzed**   **hissed**   **jumped**
> **barked**   **walked**   **smiled**   **watched**
> **hugged**   **cleaned**   **hopped**

Choose the correct words to complete each sentence. Write the words on the lines.

1. The bumble bee _____ around the room.

2. Jack _____ slowly down the bumpy road.

3. We _____ our teeth before bedtime.

4. I _____ when the dog _____ loudly.

Words to remember

Some words are not easy to read by blending the sounds of the letters. You need to learn these words by memory. See if you can remember these useful words:

because	**beautiful**	**people**
could	**clothes**	**many**	**only**
kind	**there**	**busy**

Can you spot any of the words above in the story below? Draw a ring around each word in the story.

Once upon a time there lived a kind lady.

She was busy because so many people wanted

to buy the beautiful clothes she made.

But she could only make four shirts a day.

Note for parent: Explain that these are words that we can't sound out or decode, but that we come across often. We just have to learn them!

Words that sound the same

Some words sound the same but have different meanings. Read the sentences below. Draw a ring around the correct word to complete each sentence.

Mrs Neat has one **blew / blue** car.

Mr Mac has one **sun / son**.

Jack has **two / too** cakes.

The baby has a small teddy **bare / bear**.

Note for parent: Words that sound the same, but have different meanings, are called homophones.

Coco the clown has a **flower / flour** in his hat.

Jake's boat has two big **sails / sales**.

Layla is going to **meat / meet** her friend.

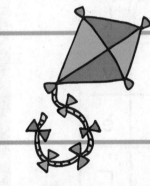

Ruby has a **red / read** and green kite.

11

Silent letters

Read the words in the box. Find each word in the grid below. Draw a ring around each word that you find. The first one has been done for you.

wrap ✓	knight	knee
know	write	wrong
knock	gnat	gnaw

k	n	i	g	h	t	b	d	f	n	k
g	q	e	n	m	m	k	c	e	r	n
u	w	q	a	d	s	n	q	h	b	o
w	r	i	t	e	l	o	u	h	g	c
t	o	c	u	u	g	w	r	a	p	k
y	n	o	w	q	w	e	w	r	t	v
h	g	n	a	w	h	t	k	n	e	e
g	q	e	d	m	m	n	c	e	r	r
b	x	e	v	q	w	r	t	y	u	k

Note for parent: In this activity your child is reading words that begin with a silent w, g or k. Explain that these spellings most likely reflect ancient pronunciation.

Adding **el**, **al** or **le**

Read the words in the box. Write each word in the correct column in the chart below. The first one has been done for you.

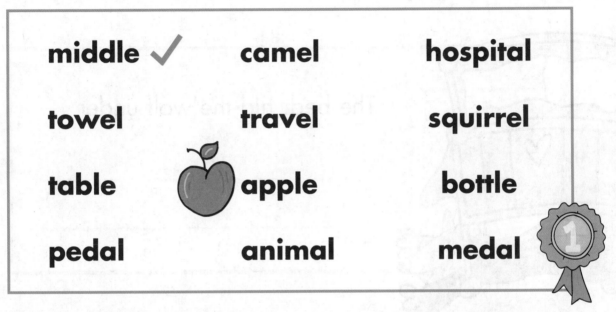

middle ✓	camel	hospital
towel	travel	squirrel
table	apple	bottle
pedal	animal	medal

el	al	le
		middle

Note for parent: This activity looks at words that have the same sounds at the end when spoken, but have different letters at the end when written.

Making sense

Read the muddled sentences below. Look at the picture and put the words in the correct order to describe each picture. Write the sentences on the lines.

The bed. hid the wolf under

_____

_____

wolf wardrobe. hid the inside The

_____

_____

Note for parent: This activity will encourage your child to check that the text makes sense to them as they read.

Ordering sentences

The story below doesn't make sense because the sentences are muddled up. Number the sentences in the correct order from 1 to 3.

But the cat scared the dog away.

A dog came along and barked at the cat.

A cat was asleep under a tree.

Note for parent: This activity encourages your child to read for meaning in order to sequence events in stories.

We sometimes combine two words into one word! When we write the new word, we use an apostrophe to show where the missing spaces and letters should be. The new word is called a 'contraction'.

For example:

I am = I'm   **I will = I'll**

Follow the lines with your finger to match each set of words to the correct contraction.

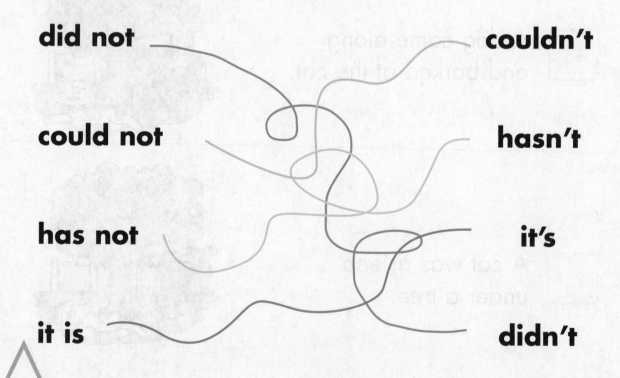

did not   **couldn't**

could not   **hasn't**

has not   **it's**

it is   **didn't**

Ordering instructions

These instructions on how to make a birthday card are not in the correct order! Read them carefully and number the instructions in the correct order from 1 to 5.

Draw a picture on the front of the card using coloured pencils.

Above the drawing on the front of the card, write the words 'Happy Birthday'.

Finally, you can sign the finished card.

Now that the front of the card is finished, write a birthday message on the inside.

First, fold a rectangle of thin card in half.

What am I?

Draw a line to match each description to the correct picture.

I can fly and hover in the air. I have blades that go round.

I can fly and hover in the air. I collect nectar and pollen to make honey.

I can fly very fast across the world. I have powerful engines.

I have feathers but I cannot fly. I use my wings to help me swim.

Who is who?

Look at the pictures of the children. Read the descriptions below and write the name of a child to complete each of the sentences.

Lucy   **Ryan**   **Ali**   **Rupert**   **Farah**

The girl wearing a spotty jumper is _____.

The boy wearing red boots is _____.

The girl with a bow in her hair is _____.

The boy wearing a hat is _____.

The boy with the stripy scarf is _____.

Note for parent: This activity requires your child to read the sentences carefully and look for clues in the picture.

19

Reading a poem

Read the poem below.

The North Wind

The north wind does blow,
And we shall have snow,
And what will poor Robin do then,
poor thing?
He'll sit in a barn,
And keep himself warm,
And hide his head under his wing,
Poor thing.

Answer these questions about the poem. Draw a ring around each correct answer.

Where did the wind come from?

the north   **the south**

Which word rhymes with 'blow'?

wing   **snow**

Why did the robin put his head under his wing?

to keep warm   **to shelter from the sun**

Draw a picture in the space below to match the words of the poem.

Note for parent: Encourage your child to look back at the poem to find the answers in the text.

21

Reading a story

Read this story about Coco the clown.

Coco was very upset.

He was the only clown in the circus who couldn't juggle, but he kept it a secret.

One day, the ringmaster asked Coco to juggle, but Coco made up an excuse.

"Okay then, but you must promise to juggle tomorrow!" said the ringmaster.

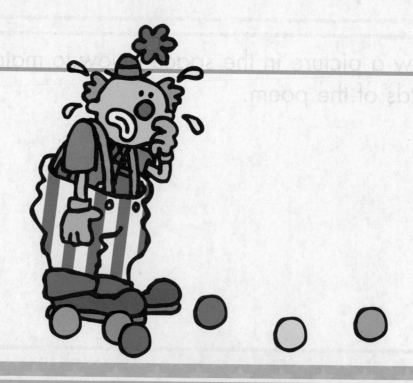

Coco's friend, Merlin the magician, had an idea.

"Repeat this spell after me," Merlin said.

"I can juggle. I can juggle. Say that one hundred times before you go to sleep tonight."

The next morning, the ringmaster said to Coco, "Can you show me how you juggle today?"

Coco nervously took the juggling balls in his hands and threw them up in the air one by one, and a wonderful thing happened.

This time, he didn't drop them.
He could juggle!

"I can juggle!" Coco said.
"I can juggle!"

Understanding a story

Read the sentences in the boxes. Choose the correct words to complete each sentence about the story on the previous pages. Draw a ring around the correct answer.

At the beginning of the story Coco was very upset because…

he couldn't juggle   **he had toothache**

The ringmaster made Coco promise to…

juggle tomorrow   **juggle next week**

Note for parent: Encourage your child to read the text on pages 22 and 23 again to help them find the answers.

Coco had to repeat the spell…

100 times   **1000 times**

Coco was helped by…

Ava the acrobat   **Merlin the magician**

The words of the spell were…

I can juggle.   **I like to juggle.**
I can juggle.   **I like to juggle.**

The ringmaster asked Coco to juggle…

the next morning   **the next afternoon**

25

Reading information

Look at the pictures and read the descriptions below. Write the correct number next to each picture to match the right description.

Nocturnal Animals

owl

fox

bat

1 Bats can't see very well, but they have excellent hearing to help them hunt in the dark.

2 Owls have large eyes to help them see in the dark. They can turn their head to look backwards when they search for food.

3 Foxes have whiskers to help them to feel around in the dark. They live in dens underground.

Read the sentences below. Choose the correct word to complete each sentence. Write the words on the lines and draw pictures of the words in the boxes.

Bats	Owls	Foxes

_____ have large eyes to help them see in the dark.

_____ live in dens underground.

_____ have excellent hearing.

Note for parent: This activity will encourage your child to relocate the information they have read in a text already.

27

Making predictions

Read the story and predict what happens next.

The Cake Sale

Jake was helping his mum get ready for a cake sale. Griff the dog looked at Jake.
"Can Griff come too?" Jake asked his mum.
"Of course," said Mum.
"Come on, then!" Jake said to the dog.
They arrived and put the cakes on a table.
Jake and his mum went to get some plates.
"Don't touch, Griff," Jake said.
Griff looked at the yummy cakes.
He sniffed the cakes. He got a bit closer.
He looked behind him to check no one could see.

Write a sentence about what you think happens next.

_____

_____

_____

Note for parent: Your child is making a prediction of what will happen next based on what they have read. Discuss the possible endings together.

Did you like the story? Circle your answer.

Yes   **No**

What did you like most or least about the story?
Draw a picture of it in the space below.

Note for parent: In this activity your child is expressing their personal opinion about the story.

29

Somebody has stolen Max Monkey's fruit. These are the possible suspects. Read their names.

Boris Bat

Polly Parrot

Molly Monkey

Ollie Owl

Read the story and the clues to work out who stole Max Monkey's fruit.

In the jungle one day, Max Monkey was feeling tired, so he left his fruit and went for a sleep. While he was gone, a thief hid the fruit under its wing and stole it! A witness said the thief had a squawky voice.

Clues:

- The thief hid the fruit under its wing.
- The theft happened in the daytime.
- A witness said the thief had a squawky voice.

Write the name of the fruit thief on the line below.

_____ stole Max Monkey's fruit.

Answers

Page 4
a spotty snake
a brown shoe
a clean piglet

Page 5
are – scare, dare
igh – night, right
air – chair, pair, hair
ore – more, before
ear – near, hear

Page 6
loudly, heavily,
carefully, friendly

Page 8
1. buzzed
2. walked OR hopped
   OR jumped
3. cleaned
4. jumped, barked

Page 9
Once upon a time **there**
lived a **kind** lady.
She was **busy because** so
many people wanted to
buy the **beautiful clothes**
she made.
But she **could only** make
four shirts a day.

Pages 10–11
Mrs Neat has one **blue** car.
Mr Mac has one **son**.
Jack has **two** cakes.
The baby has a small teddy
bear.
Coco the clown has a **flower**
in his hat.
Jake's boat has two big **sails**.
Layla is going to **meet** her
friend.
Ruby has a **red** and green kite.

Page 12

k	n	i	g	h	t	b	d	f	n	k
g	q	e	n	m	m	k	c	e	r	n
u	w	q	a	d	s	n	q	h	b	o
w	r	i	t	e	l	o	u	h	g	c
t	o	c	u	u	g	w	r	a	p	k
y	n	o	w	q	w	e	w	r	t	v
h	g	n	a	w	h	t	k	n	e	e
g	q	e	d	m	m	n	c	e	r	r
b	x	e	v	q	w	r	t	y	u	k

Page 13
el – towel, squirrel,
camel, travel
al – pedal, hospital,
animal, medal
le – middle, bottle,
apple, table

Page 14
The wolf hid under the bed.
The wolf hid inside the
wardrobe.

Page 15
1. A cat was asleep
   under a tree.
2. A dog came along and
   barked at the cat.
3. But the cat scared the
   dog away.

Page 16
did not – didn't
could not – couldn't
has not – hasn't
it is – it's

Page 17
1. First, fold a rectangle
   of thin card in half.
2. Draw a picture on
   the front of the card
   using coloured pencils.
3. Above the drawing on
   the front of the card,
   write the words
   'Happy Birthday'.
4. Now that the front of
   the card is finished,
   write a birthday
   message on the inside.
5. Finally, you can sign
   the finished card.

Page 18

Page 19
Lucy, Ryan, Farah, Rupert, Ali

Page 21
the north, snow, to keep warm

Pages 24–25
he couldn't juggle
juggle tomorrow
100 times
Merlin the magician
I can juggle. I can juggle.
the next morning

Page 26
owl – 2, fox – 3, bat – 1

Page 27
Owls, Foxes, Bats

Page 31
Polly Parrot